The Trojan Horse

Retold by Russell Punter

Illustrated by Matteo Pincelli

Reading consultant: Alison Kelly
Roehampton University

Contents

The costumes and buildings in
this version of the story come from
Classical Greece (c.500-400 B.C.),
the most popular setting for the tale.
The original story is set at the time of
the Mycenaeans – Greek people who lived
around 1600-1100 B.C.

Chapter 1

The runaway queen

Helen lived in Ancient Greece. People said she was the most beautiful woman in the world.

Helen was married to King Menelaus of Sparta. He was proud of his lovely wife.

"I want you to stay by my side forever," he told her.

One day, a young prince
named Paris came to the palace.

He was from the city of Troy,
across the Aegean Sea.

When Paris met Helen, he fell madly in love. "Come back to Troy with me," he begged.

Helen had fallen for Paris too. So she agreed to go with him.

Menelaus was furious when he found out what had happened.

"I don't care how long it takes," he roared. "I'll get Helen back."

Chapter 2

The Trojan war

All the kings of Greece agreed
to help bring Helen home.

Only Odysseus, king of Ithaca,
didn't want to be away fighting.
But the others persuaded him.

The next morning, Menelaus and the other kings set sail with their army. Hundreds of ships crossed the sea to Troy.

Many days later, the Greek ships reached land. The soldiers waded ashore and stormed up to the city.

"Now all we have to do is get inside," said Odysseus, who wanted to get home quickly. But Troy was well defended.

Time and again,
the Greeks attacked.

But, however hard they tried, they couldn't break in.

Little did they know just how long the war was set to last.

Over ten long years, a thousand ships brought more soldiers to Troy.

But the Trojans remained trapped in their city. And the Greeks were still stuck outside.

Both sides had lost many men. By now, the Greeks were beginning to give up hope.

Then Odysseus had an idea.
"It's pretty wild," he thought.
"But it might just work."

Chapter 3

A big idea

The other Greek kings agreed
to the plan. The first stage was
to cut down lots of trees.

The Greek soldiers sawed
the trees into planks. Then
they joined the planks together.

18

Piece by piece, Odysseus's idea slowly took shape.

After a week's hard work, the Greek army had built a mighty, magnificent...

...wooden horse.

Odysseus admired the men's efforts. "Now to put my plan into action," he said.

Chapter 4

Undercover

That night, the Greeks pulled the horse to the city gates.

They opened a small door in the horse's belly.

Odysseus and some of his men climbed inside.

23

One soldier named Sinon
hid nearby.

King Menelaus and the
others went back to their ships
and sailed out of sight.

The next morning, the Trojans couldn't believe their eyes.

"The Greeks have gone," cried one soldier.

"And there's a giant horse outside!" gasped another.

The Trojans ran out of the city. They gazed in wonder at the new arrival.

Sinon came out of hiding. "Who are you?" asked a soldier. "And what's this?"

"I ran away from the Greek army," lied Sinon. "They built the horse."

What's it for?

"It's a gift to the goddess Athene," said Sinon, "to bring them luck on the trip home."

"Maybe it will bring us luck too," said the Trojan soldier.

Bring it inside!

The Trojans hauled the horse into the city. The first part of Odysseus's plan was working.

Chapter 5

The army awakes

That evening, the Trojans held a big party to celebrate the end of the war.

There was feasting, dancing and singing. The celebrations went on all night.

It was early morning before the Trojans went to bed.

At last, Sinon could get to work.

He tiptoed to the horse and tapped three times on its leg.

Inside, Odysseus sprang into action. "That's the signal!" he whispered.

He opened the trap door
and led his men out.

The Greeks scurried across the
city as silently as they could.

The guards at the gates were
fast asleep. Slowly, the Greek
soldiers lifted off the bolt.

They heaved opened the doors. The rest of the Greek army was waiting outside.

"All right men," said Odysseus. "Now we attack!"

Chapter 6

The final battle

The Greek kings and their army stormed into Troy. There was nothing to stop them now.

The Greek soldiers crashed through the city looking for Helen.

They stole treasure wherever they could find it.

By the time the sleepy Trojans knew what was happening, it was too late.

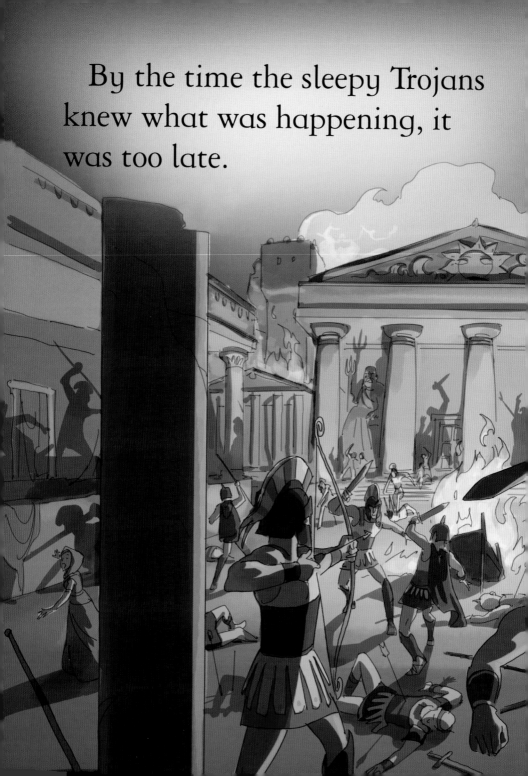

Paris rushed out to fight the Greeks. But when he saw how many there were, he ran off.

But he wasn't quick enough.
An arrow flew through the air
and struck him down dead.

"Now, where's Helen?"
wondered Menelaus.

Watching from above, Helen knew there was no possible escape from Troy.

"Perhaps the king will throw me in prison," she thought nervously. "Or worse."

Chapter 7

Return to Greece

It wasn't long before Helen was captured and brought before her husband.

Menelaus had been angry
with his wife for ten years.

But when he saw her
beautiful face, his anger
vanished in a second.

"At last," sighed Menelaus.
"Our mission is over."

The Greeks took Helen and
the Trojan treasure back to their
ships and headed for home.

Helen may not have wanted to go back to Greece. But she had no choice.

Menelaus was finally reunited with his queen, whose beauty launched a thousand ships.

The Legend of the Trojan Horse

The Trojan Horse is based on part of a poem called *The Iliad*. It was composed by a Greek poet named Homer, who lived around 800 B.C. It tells the story of a great war between Greece and Troy, a city in the country now known as Turkey.

Usborne Quicklinks

For links to websites to find out more about the Trojan horse and life in Ancient Greece, go to the Usborne Quicklinks website at **www.usborne.com/quicklinks** and enter the keywords 'trojan horse.'

Please follow the internet safety guidelines on the Usborne Quicklinks website. Usborne Publishing cannot be responsible for the content of any website other than its own. We recommend that young children are supervised while on the internet.

Historical consultant: Dr. Anne Millard
Series editor: Lesley Sims

This edition first published in 2019 by Usborne Publishing Ltd., Usborne House, 83-85 Saffron Hill, London EC1N 8RT, England. www.usborne.com Copyright © 2019, 2011 Usborne Publishing Ltd.